To ████,
Merry Christmas!
Love,
Auntie ██████, Uncle ████,
████, ██████

Monster Chef

For the kids of Wagait Beach and Belyuen—NB

Scholastic Canada Ltd.
604 King Street West, Toronto, Ontario M5V 1E1, Canada

Scholastic Inc.
557 Broadway, New York, NY 10012, USA

Scholastic Australia Pty Limited
PO Box 579, Gosford, NSW 2250, Australia

Scholastic New Zealand Limited
Private Bag 94407, Botany, Manukau 2163, New Zealand

Scholastic Children's Books
Euston House, 24 Eversholt Street, London NW1 1DB, UK

www.scholastic.ca

Nick used watercolour, gouache, pencil and pastel to create these illustrations.

Library and Archives Canada Cataloguing in Publication
Bland, Nick, 1973-, author, illustrator
Monster chef / written and illustrated by Nick Bland.
ISBN 978-1-4431-2881-0 (bound).--ISBN 978-1-4431-2882-7 (pbk.)
I. Title.
PZ7.B557Mo 2014   j823'.92   C2013-907833-9

Text and illustrations copyright © 2014 by Nick Bland.

First published by Scholastic Australia in 2014.
This edition published by Scholastic Canada Ltd. in 2014.

6 5 4 3 2 1   Printed in Malaysia 108   14 15 16 17 18

Monster Chef

Nick Bland

Scholastic Canada Ltd.
Toronto New York London Auckland Sydney
Mexico City New Delhi Hong Kong Buenos Aires

Marcel was a monster of medium size,
with crotchety horns and googly eyes.
Like most other monsters, he worked every night,
giving the neighbourhood children a fright.

His climbing was perfect . . .

his creeping was good . . .

and he hid very well,
just like all monsters should.

He was lumpy and grumpy and suitably hairy,
but Marcel had a problem . . .

He just wasn't scary.

And for those who are snarling
or snorting their snouts,

he cooks just for them . . .

...some boiled Brussels sprouts!

AHHH!